Anna's magic box

SALARIYA BOOK HOUSE

Principle 4

Chil[obscured]ghts

Anna's grandfather gave her a magic box.
'It's a secret,' he whispered. 'You will find mysterious things inside and you can be whoever you want. Can you see this little door? Here's the key. I'm too big to go through it. Only small children like you can enter this world.'

2 1

When her grandfather had left the room, Anna looked at the box. She wasn't sure what to make of it. It was very large indeed. It appeared to be made of wood, and it changed colour every time she moved it. She turned it around a few times, then finally took the key from her pocket and put it in the keyhole.

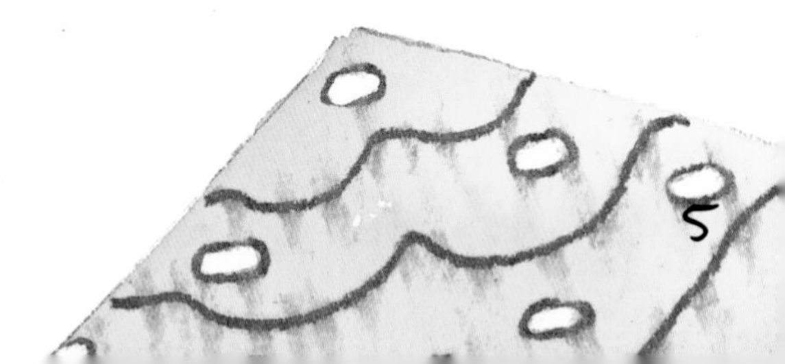

Anna suddenly found herself in a strange world. The clouds were under her feet, and the trees, flowers and bushes were hanging from the roof! Then she heard a distant cry. What was happening? She put on a detective's raincoat and hat, and with a magnifying glass she followed the trail.

A trail of tears led her to five little coloured rabbits.
'What's the matter?' she asked them.
'We're starving, but all the carrots are too high up,' replied one of the rabbits.
'And we're too small to reach them,' added another.
Anna looked through her magnifying glass at the clouds at her feet, and then she glanced up at the carrots above.

'Everything's turned upside down,' she said.
'Have you thought about turning it back?'
Anna and the rabbits started jumping up and down until everything tumbled back the right way. Now the little rabbits could reach the carrots easily.
'It was *so* easy!' squealed the five rabbits.
'Sometimes a big problem gets smaller if we think it through and try to find an answer,' Anna replied happily.

The next time Anna went into the magic box, the rabbits seemed to be exhausted.
They were running around a very high table.
'What are you doing? You'll get dizzy if you keep running around like that.'
'Oh! We'd like to stop!' wheezed one of the rabbits, breathlessly. 'But only four of us can sit at the table because there aren't enough stools.
So we don't sit down – we just keep running around it.'

This time Anna picked up a piece of chalk, just like a teacher, and taught the rabbits to count.
'One, two, three, four and five. You are five rabbits!'
They nodded their heads and Anna continued her lesson: 'One, two, three, four. There are only four stools. We need one more stool to make five.'

'What can we do?' asked one of the rabbits sadly.
'We can add one more stool or... cut down all the table legs.'
Anna put on a carpenter's overall and, with a saw in her hand, she cut the legs down to make the table lower. Now all the rabbits could reach their food.

The third time that Anna visited the colourful rabbits, she found them looking very, very pale. She put on a doctor's coat and looked at them carefully.

'What's wrong, my little rabbits?'

'We can't get to sleep,' they all sighed at the same time. 'The sun is so bright that we can't close our eyes.'
'Have you thought about sleeping when the sun sets? Or you could sleep in a burrow under the ground.'
'Oh, you're so clever!' they all squealed.

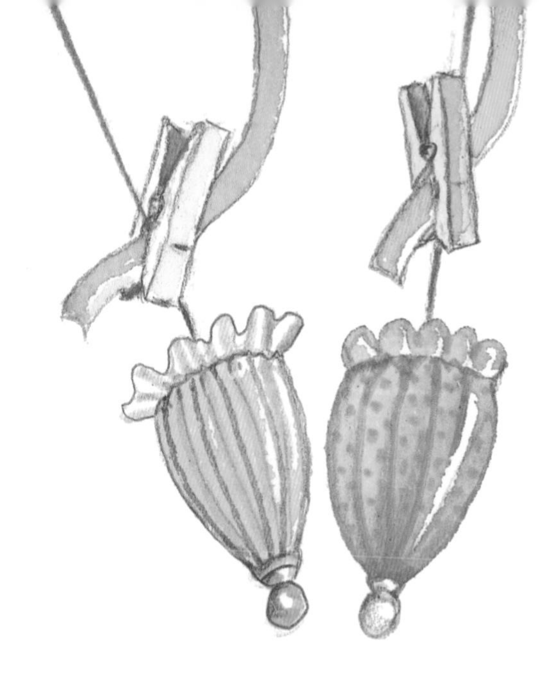

One night, the magic box was so noisy that it woke Anna. It made a banging noise as it tumbled across the floor. She went inside.

'Now what's wrong, my little friends?' she asked the rabbits.

'We're scared of the dark.'

‘Mmm... Let’s see how we can fix...’
A blinding light interrupted Anna’s thoughts: Her mother had come into her room and turned the light on.
‘Anna, what are you doing playing with grandfather’s dressing-up box? The doctor told you to stay in bed!’

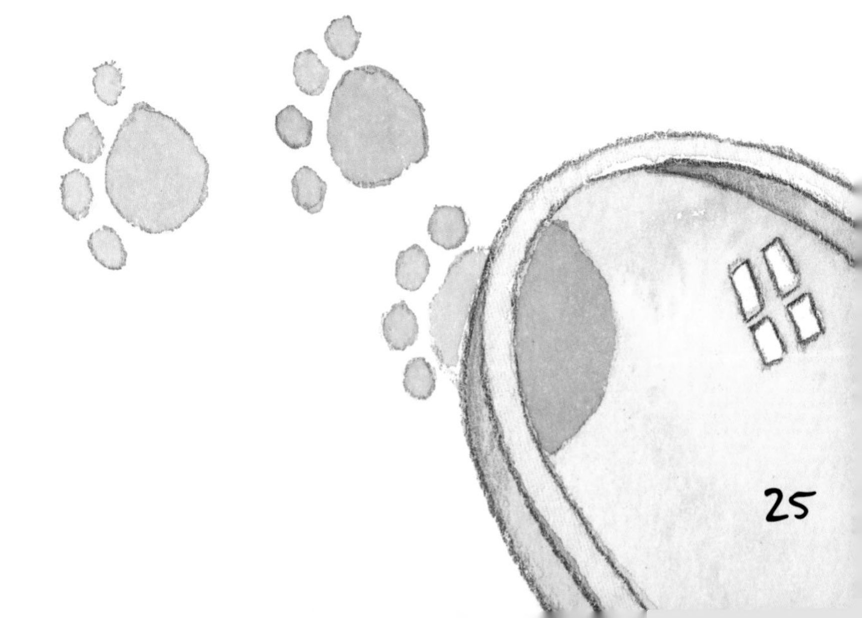

'I... I couldn't sleep,' she muttered; and, thinking of the rabbits, she quickly added: 'because of the dark...'

'Well, it's time for your medicine now and you must get back to bed. If you're good, I'll read you a story. A short one...'

'That's the answer: a story!' thought Anna. 'Why didn't I think of that?'

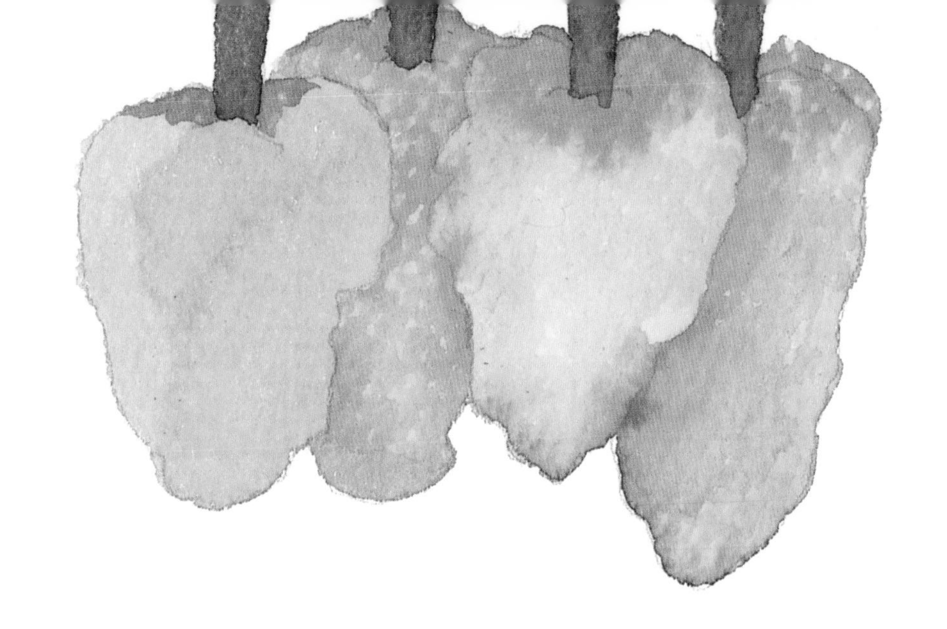

Nobody told stories better than Anna's mother. Anna looked at her mum differently tonight. She understood that being a mother, a doctor and a teacher was a lot of fun, but it was also very exhausting.
But Anna was only a girl, so she still had time to learn how to be a grown-up.

Before her mother began the story,
Anna asked her one last thing:
'Mum, can you leave the door in
the box open a little?' She wanted the
rabbits to fall asleep listening to the
bedtime story, too.
'As you wish, but get into bed, now!'
And that night, a girl and five rabbits
were soon sleeping peacefully.

Principle 4

# of Children's Rights:

The child shall enjoy the benefits of social security.

The child shall be entitled to grow and develop in health; to this end, special care and protection shall be provided both to him and to his mother, including adequate pre-natal and post-natal care. The child shall have the right to adequate nutrition, housing, recreation and medical services.

All boys and girls, wherever they live, deserve to have somebody to take care of them. They should receive medical attention, have enough food to eat, and be able to enjoy playing. In the story, Anna takes care of the five rabbits in the magic box. She makes sure that they can reach the carrots and eat the food on the table; she doesn't help them by moving the food closer, but rather by teaching them how to do it themselves. Anna also wants them to have enough rest and not to fall sick. Through this magical journey, she realises just how many people take care of children, from parents to teachers and doctors.

Children's Rights

Adopted by the General Assembly of the United Nations in Resolution 1386 (XIV) of 10 December 1959.

PREAMBLE

I. *Whereas* the peoples of the United Nations have, in the Charter, reaffirmed their faith in fundamental human rights and in the dignity and worth of the human person, and have determined to promote social progress and better standards of life in larger freedom,

II. *Whereas* the United Nations has, in the Universal Declaration of Human Rights, proclaimed that everyone is entitled to all the rights and freedoms set forth therein, without distinction of any kind, such as race, colour, sex, language, religion, political or other opinion, national or social origin, property, birth or other status,

III. *Whereas* the child, by reason of his physical and mental immaturity, needs special safeguards and care, including appropriate legal protection, before as well as after birth,

IV. *Whereas* the need for such special safeguards has been stated in the Geneva Declaration of the Rights of the Child of 1924, and recognised in the Universal Declaration of Human Rights and in the statutes of specialised agencies and international organisations concerned with the welfare of children,

V. *Whereas* mankind owes to the child the best it has to give,

VI. Now, therefore, *The General Assembly* proclaims this Declaration of the Rights of the Child to the end that he may have a happy childhood and enjoy for his own good and for the good of society the rights and freedoms herein set forth, and calls upon parents, upon men and women as individuals. And upon voluntary organisations, local authorities and national Governments to recognise these rights and strive for their observance by legislative and other measures progressively taken in accordance with the following principles:

Principle 1
The child shall enjoy all the rights set forth in this Declaration. Every child, without any exception whatsoever, shall be entitled to these rights, without distinction or discrimination on account of race, colour, sex, language, religion, political or other opinion, national or social origin, property, birth or other status, whether of himself or of his family.

Principle 2
The child shall enjoy special protection, and shall be given opportunities and facilities, by law and by other means, to enable him to develop physically, mentally, morally, spiritually and socially in a healthy and normal manner and in conditions of freedom and dignity. In the enactment of laws for this purpose, the best interests of the child shall be the paramount consideration.

Principle 3
The child shall be entitled from his birth to a name and a nationality.

Principle 4
The child shall enjoy the benefits of social security. He shall be entitled to grow and develop in health; to this end, special care and protection shall be provided both to him and to his mother, including adequate pre-natal and post-natal care.

The child shall have the right to adequate nutrition, housing, recreation and medical services.

Principle 5
The child who is physically, mentally or socially handicapped shall be given the special treatment, education and care required by his particular condition.

Principle 6
The child, for the full and harmonious development of his personality, needs love and understanding. He shall, wherever possible, grow up in the care and under the responsibility of his parents, and, in any case, in an atmosphere of affection and of moral and material security; a child of tender years shall not, save in exceptional circumstances, be separated from his mother. Society and the public authorities shall have the duty to extend particular care to children without a family and to those without adequate means of support. Payment of State and other assistance towards the maintenance of children of large families is desirable.

Principle 7
The child is entitled to receive education, which shall be free and compulsory, at least in the elementary stages. He shall be given an education which will promote his general culture, and enable him, on a basis of equal opportunity, to develop his abilities, his individual judgement, and his sense of moral and social responsibility, and to become a useful member of society.

The best interests of the child shall be the guiding principle of those responsible for his education and guidance; that responsibility lies in the first place with his parents.

The child shall have full opportunity for play and recreation, which should be directed to the same purposes as education; society and the public authorities shall endeavour to promote the enjoyment of this right.

Principle 8
The child shall in all circumstances be among the first to receive protection and relief.

Principle 9
The child shall be protected against all forms of neglect, cruelty and exploitation. He shall not be the subject of traffic, in any form.

The child shall not be admitted to employment before an appropriate minimum age; he shall in no case be caused or permitted to engage in any occupation or employment which would prejudice his health or education, or interfere with his physical, mental or moral development.

Principle 10
The child shall be protected from practices which may foster racial, religious and any other form of discrimination. He shall be brought up in a spirit of understanding, tolerance, friendship among peoples, peace and universal brotherhood, and in full consciousness that his energy and talents should be devoted to the service of his fellow men.

Published in Great Britain in MMXIII by
Book House, an imprint of
The Salariya Book Company Ltd
25 Marlborough Place, Brighton BN1 1UB
www.salariya.com
www.book-house.co.uk

1 3 5 7 9 8 6 4 2

A CIP catalogue record for this book is available from the British Library.

Printed and bound in China.

PB ISBN: 978-1-908973-29-0